This

Disney Annual 2015

belongs to

....

....

EGMONT
We bring stories to life

First published in 2014 by Egmont UK Limited,
1 Nicholas Road, London W11 4AN
All rights reserved.

© 2014 Disney/Pixar. Materials and characters from the movies Monsters, Inc. and Monsters University copyright © 2014 Disney/Pixar. Materials and characters from the movies Planes and Planes 2 copyright © 2014 Disney. Materials and characters from Toy Story, Toy Story 2 and Toy Story 3 copyright © 2014 Disney/Pixar. Mr. and Mrs Potato Head® is a registered trademark of Hasbro, Inc. Used with permission. © Hasbro, Inc. Materials and characters from the movies Cars and Cars 2 copyright © 2014 Disney/Pixar. Disney/Pixar elements © 2014 Disney/Pixar, not including underlying vehicles owned by third parties: AMC, Pacer and Gremlin are trademarks of Chrysler LLC. ©Volkswagen AG; Hudson Hornet™; Chevrolet™; Porsche™; Mercury™; Plymouth Superbird™; Petty™. All rights reserved.

Activities and story adaptations by Brenda Apsley.
Designed by Jeannette O'Toole.
Created for Egmont UK Limited by Ruby Shoes Limited.

ISBN 978 1 4052 7200 1
57507/1

Stay safe online. Any website addresses listed in this book are correct at the time of going to print. However, Egmont is not responsible for content hosted by third parties. Please be aware that online content can be subject to change and websites can contain content that is unsuitable for children. We advise that all children are supervised when using the internet.

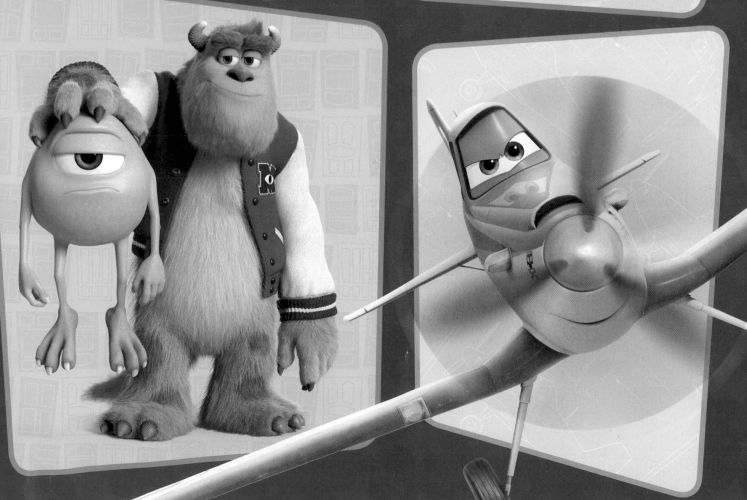

Come on, let's have fun!

Contents

Toy Story   8

Lookee Here!   10

Get Busy with Buzz   11

Which Way?   12

Poster: The Roundup Gang   13

Poster: Sunnyside Here We Come!   14

Lotsa Lotsos!   15

Story: Bonnie's Birthday Surprise   16

Mr Potato Head   20

Rex   21

What Do You Know?   22

Cars   24

Route 66   26

Tractor Tipping   28

Poster: Lightning McQueen   29

Poster: Cars 2   30

The Pit Crew   31

Let's Race!   32

Story: Mater the Greater   34

Vrooooom!   37

Quiz Challenge   38

Disney · PIXAR

TOY STORY

Disney · PIXAR

Cars

Disney · PIXAR MONSTERS

Monsters, Inc.	40
Who's Hiding?	42
Super-Scary Monster!	43
Story: Super Scarebot	44
Poster: Mike, Sulley and Boo	47
Poster: Monsters University	48
Story: When Mike Met Sulley	49
The OKs	52

Disney PLANES

Planes	54
Dusty Crophopper	55
Story: Vita-Minamulch Signals	56
Wings Around The Globe	60
Poster: Let's Soar!	61
Poster: Race to the Rescue!	62
Planes 2	63
Dusty's Second Chance	64
The Air Attack Team	66
Answers	67

Disney · PIXAR
TOY STORY

Meet the stars of Toy Story!

Toys have a secret life when we are not around!

When space ranger Buzz Lightyear takes cowboy Woody's place as Andy's best toy, Woody tries to get rid of him. But they get lost! Can they find the way home?

In **Toy Story 2** Woody is stolen by a toy collector who plans to send him to Japan. Can his toy friends rescue him?

In **Toy Story 3** the toys end up at Sunnyside Daycare. It's not a nice place, so they escape, and start a new life with a girl called Bonnie.

We're Andy's toys! From now on we stick together!

Woody the cowboy is the leader of the toys.
Bullseye, Woody's horse, rides like the wind.

Buzz Lightyear is a toy who thinks he's a real space ranger.

Jessie the yodelling cowgirl is part of Woody's Roundup Gang.

Glad to meet ya!

Buzz Lightyear, at your service! To infinity, and beyond!

Rex the green dinosaur has a big heart and a small roar.

It's not my fault!

Answer these questions to get your deputy badge. Check the answers on page 67 then tick ✔ each one you got right.

1. Who was Andy's favourite before Buzz arrived?

2. Is Bullseye a horse?

3. What is the name of the cowgirl?

Did you get 3 ticks? Yippee! Write your name on the badge.

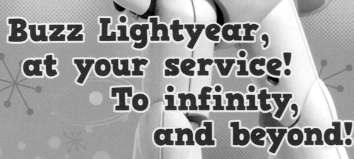

You're my favourite deputy!

9

Lookee Here!

The gang's all here!

Look at the little pictures at the bottom of this page. Which ones can you find in the big picture? Tick ✔ ONLY the ones you can see.

a ✔

b

c

d

e

Answers are on page 67.

Get Busy with Buzz

Colour in the big picture of Buzz using the small one as a guide.

Buzz says,

"To infinity, and _____!"

Can you say the missing word in your best Buzz voice? Is it:

a behind ☐   **b** beyond ☐   **c** before ☐

Write the word on the line if you like.

Answer on page 67.

Which Way?

A cowboy needs his horse! Can you help Woody find a way through the maze to Bullseye?

Woody

START →

Bullseye

→ FINISH

Answer on page 67.

SHERIFF Woody

The Roundup Gang

© Disney/Pixar

Lotsa Lotsos!

Lots-o-Huggin' Bear is called *Lotso* for short. He's the boss at Sunnyside Daycare and his smile hides a meaner side. Which Lotso looks a bit mean?

a

b

c

d

e

f

I'M A HUGGER!

Answer on page 67.

Bonnie's Birthday Surprise

Script: Tea Orsi; Layout & ink: Valentino Forlini; Colour: Mara Damiani

Mr Potato Head

Kind Mr Potato Head
adopted 3 aliens like this one.
Colour in the other 2 below
to make 3.

Oooooooooooooooooooo!

Rex

Which 2 pictures
of Rex are just
the same?

Answer on page 67.

What Do You Know?

What do you know about Woody and his friends?

1 This piggy bank thinks he knows everything about everything! What is his name?

a Hamm ☐

b Buzz ☐

c Rex ☐

2 Woody's horse is called Bullseye. Write ✔ for true or ✗ for false.

True ☐

False ☐

3 In the story Bonnie's Birthday Surprise on page 16, who fixed the cake using his tail?

4 How many aliens did Mr Potato Head adopt? Colour in a number.

1 2 3 4 5

5 What kind of toy is the boss of Sunnyside Daycare? Can you say his name?

6 Who owns Woody and the other toys?

7 Whose feet are these?

a

b

c

8 Is Rex a green dinosaur or a brown horse?

Answers are on page 67.

23

Disney · PIXAR
Cars

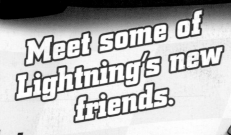

Young racer Lightning McQueen wants to be famous! When he races in the Piston Cup Challenge the result comes down to the last race.

But when he gets lost in Radiator Springs he wrecks the road, and has to stay to repair it.

Lightning's new friends show him that fame is not everything. Teamwork and friendship are more important.

In the final race, can Lightning become a true champion? *Sure he can! The winner!*

Meet some of Lightning's new friends.

Mater is a tow truck with a big heart, who's always ready to help.

Sally is a clever lawyer and owns the Cozy Cone Motel.

Doc Hudson runs the medical clinic, and knows a lot about racing.

Whoa! Guido the forklift is small, but he's strong, too. Count the tyres, and colour in the number.

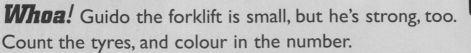

1 2 3 4 5

After Lightning wins the Piston Cup Challenge he races in the World Grand Prix. It will decide if he's the fastest car in the world.
Winning won't be easy: this is a test of skills, speed ... and heart.

Number 95, Lightning McQueen, lines up against ...

1 **Francesco Bernoulli, ITALY**

06 **Raoul CaRoule, FRANCE**

7 **Shu Todoroki, JAPAN**

4 **Max Schnell, GERMANY**

SPY!

Acer and Grem are up to no good, but secret agent Finn McMissile is on their trail!
Can you spy their names in the grid?
Look for **Grem** and **Acer**.

Clue: Look for the big letters A and G first.

z	s	A	l
w	p	c	q
G	r	e	m
o	t	r	x

Answers are on page 67.

25

Route 66

When Lightning got lost, he ended up on an old road called Route 66.

a

ROUTE 66

FLAGSTAFF
15 miles

b

LOS ANGELES
623 miles

SPRINGFIELD
1502 miles

RADIATOR SPRINGS
5 miles

CHICAGO
1502 miles

TULSA
345 miles

SANTA FE
154 miles

c

d

Can you answer these questions about the map?

1 Are these cars on the map? Write ✔ for yes, and ✘ for no.

a Doc Hudson [ ]   **b** Sally [ ]   **c** The King [ ]

d Guido [ ]   **e** Ramone [ ]   **f** Sheriff [ ]

2 How many red GAS pumps can you count? Colour in the number.

1 2 3 4 5

3 Count the green GAS pumps and draw a circle around the number.

1   2   3   4   5

4 Look at the sign in section d. How many miles to Tulsa?
Tick ✔ the answer.

a 345 [ ]   **b** 402 [ ]   **c** 123 [ ]

Answers are on page 67.

Tractor Tipping

When he's not busy towing, or being the world's best backwards driver, Mater goes ... tractor tipping!

a How many tractors has he tipped?

b How many are still the right way up?

c How many tractors altogether?

Write a number in each tyre.

Answers are on page 67.

© Disney/Pixar

The Pit Crew

Meet the Pit Crew, the fix-it friends who keep Lightning in the race! These pictures of Mater, Guido, Luigi and Fillmore look the same, but 6 things are different in picture 2. Can you spot them?

Answers are on page 67.

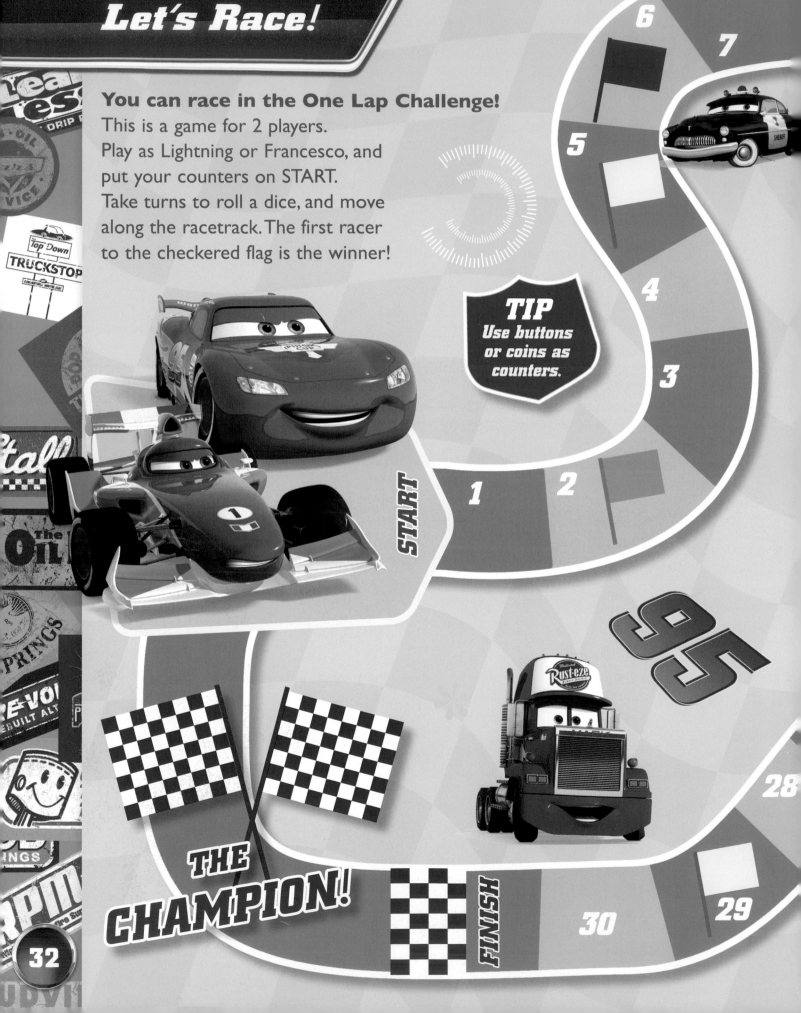

Let's Race!

You can race in the One Lap Challenge!
This is a game for 2 players.
Play as Lightning or Francesco, and
put your counters on START.
Take turns to roll a dice, and move
along the racetrack. The first racer
to the checkered flag is the winner!

TIP
Use buttons
or coins as
counters.

START

1 2 3 4 5 6 7

95

28

29

30

FINISH

THE CHAMPION!

IF YOU LAND ON ...

miss a turn

go back to the start

go forward 2 spaces

have an extra turn

Mater the Greater

WHOOAAH!

1 Lightning and his friends were at Flo's one afternoon when suddenly Mater flew past them! "Whooaah!" screamed Mater.

2 "Are you all right?" Lightning asked his friend. "Of course I'm all right!" replied Mater. "I used to be a daredevil, ya know!"

THUD!

3 Mater began to tell his story. "Here he is, Mater the Greater," said the announcer as Mater rolled into the stadium.

4 Mater hit the ramp at full speed and – whoosh! – he was airborne! But he landed on the cars below with a thud.

Cans
How many can you count here?

WHEEEEE!

5 Next, Mater was shot out of a cannon. He nearly fried his fenders in the flames. But the crowd loved it! They cheered loudly.

6 For the grand finale, Mater did a high dive jump. "He's unbelievable!" shouted the announcer. The crowd went wild!

AHHHHH!

7 "The biggest jump I ever done was Carburettor Canyon," said Mater. "Don't you remember, Lightning? You was with me!"

8 "We had rockets strapped to our backs," laughed Mater, "and you went blasting through the canyon screaming so loud!"

Answer on page 67.

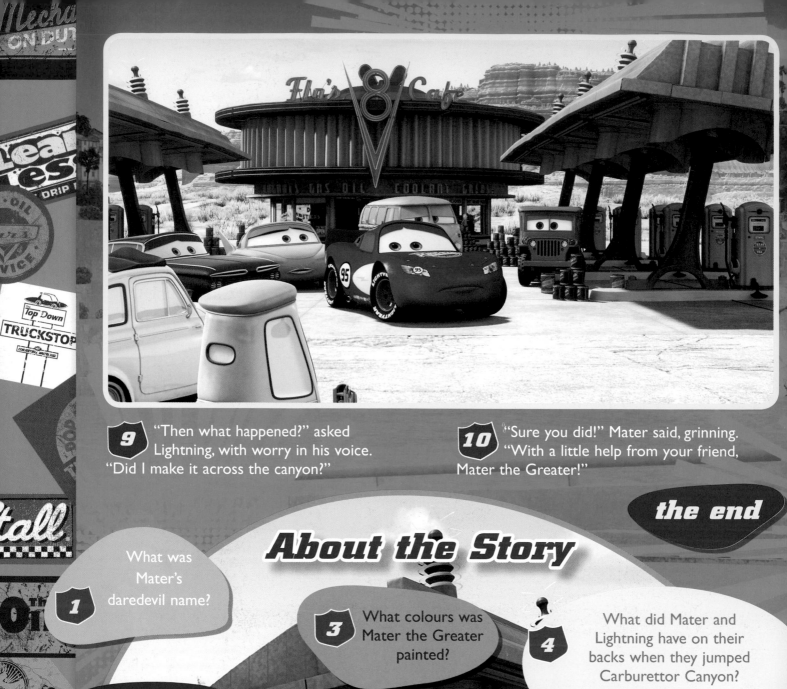

9 "Then what happened?" asked Lightning, with worry in his voice. "Did I make it across the canyon?"

10 "Sure you did!" Mater said, grinning. "With a little help from your friend, Mater the Greater!"

the end

About the Story

1 What was Mater's daredevil name?

2 Did the crowd like Mater the Greater?

3 What colours was Mater the Greater painted?

4 What did Mater and Lightning have on their backs when they jumped Carburettor Canyon?

5 Did Lightning make it across the canyon?

Answers are on page 67.

Vrooooom!

Ramone changes his own paint all the time. But the race car he'd really like to work on is … Lightning. You can beat him to it! Draw and colour in a new look for Lightning, and write your name on the line.

Lightning
by

....

Who?
Whose shadow is this?
Tick ✔ the correct box.

a

b

c

37

Answer on page 67.

Quiz Challenge

Are you up for the Quiz Challenge?

1 What does Mater like tipping?
Tick ✔ a box.

a tractors ☐   **b** tow trucks ☐   **c** taxis ☐

2 Shu Todoroki comes from Japan. Write ✔ for true or ✗ for false. ☐

3 Who owns the Cozy Cone Motel?

4 Can you match the race cars to their numbers?
Write a number for each one.

1   **2**   **3**   **4**

a 06 ☐   **b** 95 ☐   **c** 4 ☐   **d** 1 ☐

5 Who is this?

6 Which of these is NOT a member of the Pit Crew? Tick ✔ a box.

a Mater ☐

b Luigi ☐

c Sheriff ☐

7 What is the number of the road that takes Lightning to Radiator Springs? Tick ✔ a box.

a Route 7 ☐

b Route 66 ☐

c Route 16 ☐

Greetings from RADIATOR SPRINGS

GATEWAY TO THE ORNAMENT VALLEY

8 Who am I? I am a brown tow truck. My name begins with M.

Answers are on page 67.

Monsters, Inc.

Monstropolis is powered by children's screams! Monsters, Inc. is the largest scream factory in the monster world. Meet Sulley and Mike, who work there, and their friend Boo!

Arrrrrrrrrgh!

James P. Sullivan, or Sulley, is big, loud and hairy. He loves scaring, and he's Monsters, Inc.'s Top Scarer.

Sulley's my name, scaring's my game!

Sulley's Scare Assistant is **Mike Wazowski**, a little green one-eyed monster. He's part of the top Scream Team.

Not bad for a little guy!

Monsters think children are dangerous. So when a little girl called **Boo** comes into their world, they are very scared!

Sulley and Mike have to get Boo out of Monstropolis and back to her home. It's not going to be easy!

Boo! I'm Boo!

40

Sulley and Mike have special ID cards to access all areas of Monsters, Inc. Answer these questions to earn your pass!

Check the answers on page 68 then tick ✔ each question you got right.

MONSTERS, INC.
JAMES P. SULLIVAN
0069-0421-2000
SCARER
SCARE FLOOR F

MONSTERS, INC.
MIKE WAZOWSKI
0061-0210-2000
SCARE ASSISTANT
SCARE FLOOR F

1 *Who is Sulley's Scare Assistant?*

2 *Is Boo a girl or a boy?*

3 *Who is Monsters, Inc.'s Top Scarer?*

If you get 3 ticks, write your name on the pass, and draw your picture or add a photo.

ACCESS ALL AREAS

M

MONSTERS, INC.

Who's Hiding?

Which doors are Boo, Sulley and Mike hiding behind?
Write a number in each box.

Can you guess which sea monster is
behind door 6? Clue: it has 8 arms!

Answers are on page 68.

Super-Scary Monster!

Purple hair? 3 horns? 1 big eye? Draw and colour in your most super-scary scream-extractor monster! Write your name on the line.

Arrrrgh!

My monster by

_____

Super Scarebot

1 One morning, on the Scare Floor at Monsters, Inc., Waternoose made an announcement. "You've been working far too hard lately, Sulley," he said.

"Have I? Well, I do try my best, sir!" Sulley replied. Waternoose nodded and showed Sulley a new robot. "Meet Super Scarebot," Waternoose announced.

2 "The Super Scarebot is just as good as the top Scarers," Waternoose told Sulley, "plus he never gets tired! Just stand back and watch him do his best work!"

3 "The Super Scarebot will be a big help!" Mike laughed, as he collected the scream canisters. "Now you can take a break any time you like, Sulley!"

4 But Sulley wasn't impressed. "I don't need a robot's help," he shouted, as he marched past the Scarebot and through a door to collect a new scream.

5 Mike told Sulley to let the Scarebot help him, so Sulley took a break. He got very bored sitting around and waiting for the Scarebot to finish his work, though.

6 "I'm tired of waiting for a robot to do my job!" Sulley groaned. "Now it's your turn!" Mike shouted. "The Scarebot's been in that room for too long!"

7 Sulley rushed into the room and found the Super Scarebot playing with a boy! "This boy loves robots!" the Scarebot sighed. "I can't escape!"

45

8 As the Scarebot and the boy played, Sulley made his scariest face. Straight away the boy jumped off the Scarebot and ran back to his bed, screaming.

9 On the Scare Floor, Sulley explained that the Super Scarebot wasn't scary enough. "I should have known I couldn't replace you, Sulley!" Waternoose chuckled.

the end

About the Story

1 What was the robot called?

2 Why was Sulley bored?

3 What did the boy love?

4 Who made his scariest face?

Answers are on page 68.

MONSTERS, INC.

We scare because we care!

PNK
PYTHON NU KAPPA

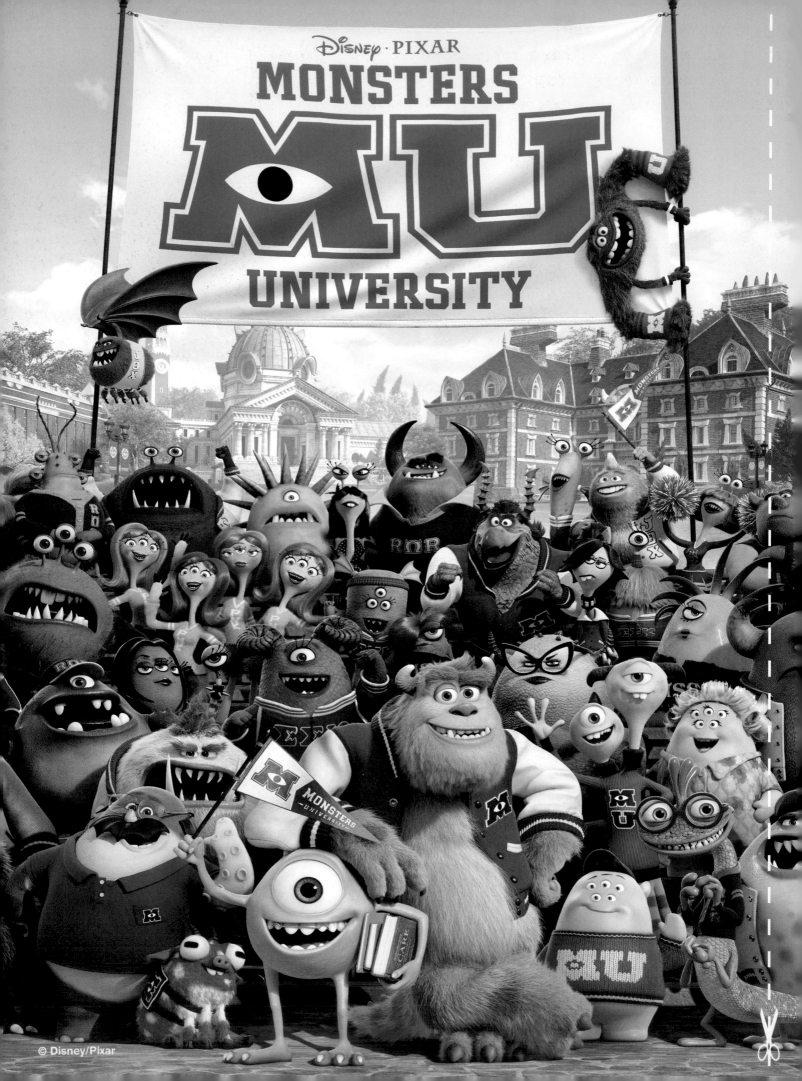

When Mike Met Sulley

1 Ever since Mike was a little monster, he dreamed of attending Monsters University. When Mike's dream came true, he couldn't wait to begin classes.

2 Mike was in the Scaring Programme at MU. In his first class, he noticed a big blue monster arriving late. That monster was known as Sulley!

3 Mike wasn't a big monster so he had to study extra hard to learn how to scare kids. He spent every waking moment preparing for his exams.

4 But Sulley just relaxed and ate pizza. He was a big monster with a loud roar, so he thought he could pass his exams without studying.

5 One night, Sulley climbed into Mike's room, mistaking it for his own. Mike was studying as usual and didn't want to be interrupted.

6 MU's rival school, Fear Tech, had a mascot called Archie the Scare Pig. Sulley stole him, but he escaped, and made a mess of Mike's room.

7 Archie ran all over the place, and when Mike tried to catch him, he ended up riding Archie on a wild chase through the fraternity house!

8 Mike finally trapped Archie, and Sulley held them both above his head, laughing! Sulley and Mike still didn't like each other very much, but eventually they become best friends!

the end

About the Story

1 What university does Mike go to?

2 What is the name of the blue monster who arrives late at class?

3 Does Sulley study hard?

4 Does Mike study hard?

5 Who made a mess of Mike's room?

Answers are on page 68.

The OKs

Mike and Sulley's student group at Monsters University is called Oozma Kappa – the OKs.
Can you match the sets of clues to their names? Write in the letters if you like.

Terri and Terry

1

I wear glasses.
I wear a green top.
I have a moustache.

Who am I?

D _ _

2

I have 5 eyes.
I have 1 ear.
I have 3 eyebrows.

Who am I?

S _ _ _ _ _ _

Don

Squishy

Art

3

I am covered in purple fur.
I have 4 fingers on each hand.
I have lots of teeth.

Who am I?

A _ _ _

4

We have 2 heads
and 1 body.
We have 2 eyes.
We have 7 legs.

Who are we?

T _ _ _ _ _

and T _ _ _ _ _

Answers are on page 68.

53

Disney PLANES

Dusty Crophopper

Skipper

Dusty Crophopper is a crop-dusting plane who enters the Wings Around The Globe Rally. But he needs help if he's going to beat the top flyers!

A plane called Skipper helps him. "Remember," he says, "it ain't how fast ya fly, it's how ya fly fast! Show me what ya got!"

But when Skipper tells Dusty to fly higher, he's scared. "I'm afraid of heights!" says Dusty.

The race is long and hard, but after many miles and many days, Dusty is the winner!

"Not too bad for a farm boy!" says Dusty.

What is Dusty afraid of? Tick ✔ the right answer.

a hippos

b heights

c hens

Answer on page 68.

Dusty Crophopper

Dusty sprays a special powder called Vita-minamulch on fields to make crops grow well. Which picture shows him working? How do you know?

a

b

c

d

e

Answer on page 68.

55

Vita-Minamulch Signals

57

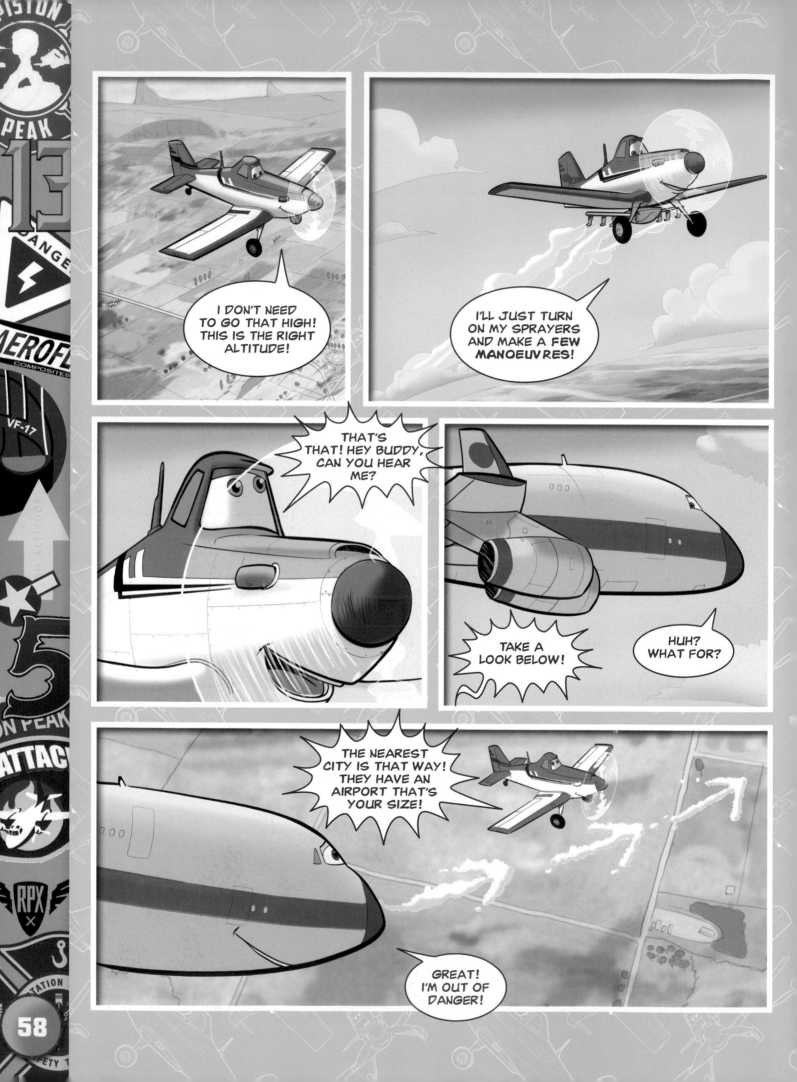

Wings Around The Globe

Dusty flew all over the world.
Can you find some names
of places he visited?
They are spelled out from
left to right and from top to bottom.
Tick ✔ each name when you find it.

Clue: Look for the big letters C, M, N and I first.

M	e	x	i	c	o
d	C	b	m	N	y
t	h	u	p	e	h
v	i	k	j	p	w
I	n	d	i	a	s
r	a	x	t	l	z

China ☐

Mexico ☐

Nepal ☐

India ☐

Answers are on page 68.

LET'S SOAR!

Disney PLANES 2

Three years ago, Dusty won the Wings Around The Globe Rally, and now he's a famous racer. But his life changes when his engine is damaged. Are his racing days over? What will he do now? Read the story on page 64 to find out.

Use the spot colours to add orange and blue to complete this picture of Dusty.

Dusty's Second Chance

You can help read Dusty's story. Listen to the words and when you come to a picture, say the name.

Dusty   **Blade Ranger**   **Patch**   **Smokejumpers**

can't race any more, but he wants to be useful.

meets   , a fire and rescue helicopter

and the leader of the air attack team.

wants to join, but first   has to teach

some new skills. One day,   hears a radio message

from   .

"FIRE! FIRE!" says . It's an emergency!

helps fight the big wild fire.

Brave fight the fire on the ground.

When the get trapped, helps

rescue them. It is dangerous, and is a true hero!

crashes, and is hurt, but when he gets better he

hears good news. has a new gearbox, and

says he has passed his tests! has a

second chance, and starts his new life as a fire fighter!

The end

The Air Attack Team

Dusty loves his new life in the air attack team.
How much do you know about them?

1 Lil' Dipper is a super-scooper. What colour is she?
Tick ✔ a spot.

⬤ ⬤ ⬤ ⬤

2 Who is the leader of the team?

3 In the story on page 64, who sent the radio message about the fire?

4 Can you draw lines to match the flyers to their shadows?

66

Answers

page 9
Toy Story

1. Woody
2. Yes
3. Jessie

page 10
Lookee Here!
a, d and e

page 11
Get Busy with Buzz
b, beyond!

page 12
Which Way?
Here is one way through the maze. There are other ways, too!

page 15
Lotsa Lotsos
Lotso e looks a bit mean

page 21
Rex
2 and 7 are the same

page 22-23
What Do You Know?
1. a, Hamm
2. True
3. Rex
4. 3
5. He's a bear called Lotso
6. Andy
7. a, Buzz; b, Rex; c, Woody
8. Rex is a green dinosaur

pages 24-25
Cars
There are 4 tyres

z	s	A	l
w	p	c	q
G	r	e	m
o	t	r	x

pages 26-27
Route 66
1. a, Doc Hudson; c, The King; e, Ramone; f, Sheriff
2. 3
3. 2
4. a, 345

page 28
Tractor Tipping
a, 3; b, 5; c, 8

page 31
The Pit Crew

page 35
Mater the Greater
There are 4 cans

page 36
About the Story
1. Mater the Greater
2. Yes
3. Red, white and blue
4. Rockets
5. Yes

page 37
Vrooooom!
a, Raoul CaRoule

pages 38-39
Quiz Challenge
1. a, Tractors
2. True
3. Sally
4. 1b; 2d; 3c; 4a
5. Finn McMissile
6. c, Sheriff
7. b, Route 66
8. Mater

Answers

page 41
Monsters, Inc.
1. Mike Wazowski
2. A girl
3. James P. Sullivan (Sulley)

page 42
Who's Hiding?
Boo: door 3
Mike: door 1
Sulley: door 4
An octopus is behind door 6

page 46
About the Story
1. Super Scarebot
2. He was waiting for the Scarebot to do his work
3. Robots
4. Sulley

page 50
When Mike Met Sulley
Mike has read 8 books

page 51
About the Story
1. Monsters University or MU
2. Sulley
3. No
4. Yes
5. Archie the Scare Pig

page 52
The OKs
1. Don
2. Squishy
3. Art
4. Terri and Terry

PLANES

page 54
Planes
b, heights

page 55
Dusty Crophopper
d; he is using his sprayers

page 60
Wings Around The Globe

page 66
The Air Attack Team

1.

2. Blade Ranger

3. Patch

4.

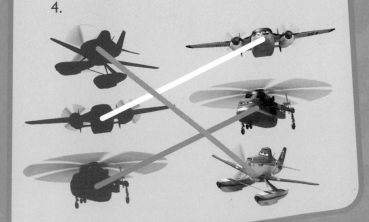